Silver Burdett Ginn Science

DISCOVERYWORKS

TEACHER RESOURCE BOOK

GRADE 1

HOME-SCHOOL CONNECTION

SCIENCE NOTEBOOK

ACTIVITY SUPPORT

ASSESSMENT GUIDE

UNIT PROJECT PAGES

Silver Burdett Ginn
PARSIPPANY, NJ   NEEDHAM, MA
Atlanta, GA   Deerfield, IL   Irving, TX   Santa Clara, CA

UNIT **C**

MAGNETS

CREDITS
Contributing artists
Benton Mahan, Bill Basso, Mike Dammer, John Kilgrew

 Silver Burdett Ginn
A Division of Simon & Schuster
299 Jefferson Road, P.O. Box 480
Parsippany, NJ 07054-0480

ISBN 0-382-33632-1

1 2 3 4 5 6 7 8 9 10 BW 05 04 03 02 01 00 99 98 97 96 95

CONTENTS

Magnets

Magnets

OVERVIEW
Home-School Connection

The Home-School Connection component of **Science DiscoveryWorks** forges a link between the equally powerful learning environments of home and school. By sharing the child's science lessons with family members, the Home-School Connection demonstrates to children that science is not just something that takes place in a school classroom. Children find that the science they learn in the classroom is a reflection of what happens in their homes, in their neighborhoods, and in the rest of the world.

The Home-School Connection is one of the ways in which **Science DiscoveryWorks** encourages families to get involved in the learning process. Each Explore at Home activity will be fun for both children and family members. Because these activities are designed to require only small amounts of time, inexpensive materials, and little previous scientific knowledge, the activities allow *all* families to participate in the education of their children. The Home-School Connection extends each unit by encouraging children to continue exploring the unit topic at home.

The Home-School Connection component includes a Unit Opening Letter, an Explore at Home activity for each lesson, and a Unit Closing Letter.

Unit Opening Letter

This letter introduces the family to the topic their child will be studying. The letter, sent home at the beginning of the unit, alerts family members to watch for relevant news stories or life examples that reinforce the material as the *child is learning it*, and links the topic to the real world. The Unit Opening Letter also encourages families to participate with the school learning experience by donating household items for classroom activities or by sharing their time or experiences with the class.

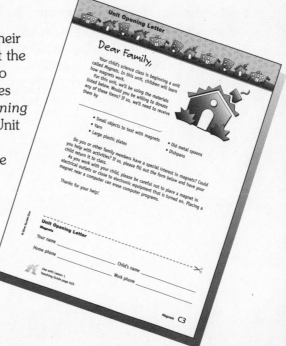

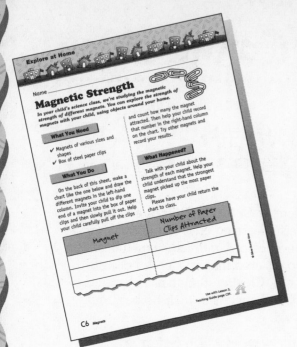

Explore at Home

Each Explore at Home activity presents an opportunity for children and family members to work together. By focusing on activities, games, or simple experiments that will be fun for both children and family members, the Explore at Home activities encourage families to get involved. Addressed to the family, every Explore at Home activity summarizes the objective of the activity and explains what children should understand after completing the activity. The activities use materials that are inexpensive and readily available, and do not require family members to have an extensive science background. While these activities would ideally engage both the child and family, most can be done by the child alone. There is one Explore at Home activity for each lesson.

Unit Closing Letter

At the end of each unit, a Unit Closing Letter provides the family with some options for delving further into the unit topic. These suggestions may include a family field trip to a zoo or a museum, some simple experiments, or books that the family may enjoy reading together. The letter invites child and family to look for real-world applications of unit material, and to continue exploring the topic after that unit of study has been completed in the classroom.

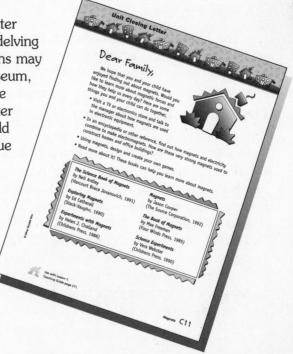

Dear Family,

Your child's science class is beginning a unit called *Magnets*. In this unit, children will learn how magnets work.

For this unit, we'll be using the materials listed below. Would you be willing to donate any of these items? If so, we'll need to receive them by

_____.

- Small objects to test with magnets
- Yarn
- Large plastic plates

- Old metal spoons
- Dishpans

Do you or other family members have a special interest in magnets? Could you help with activities? If so, please fill out the form below and have your child return it to class.

As you work with your child, please be careful not to place a magnet in electrical outlets or close to electronic equipment that is turned on. Placing a magnet near a computer can erase computer programs.

Thanks for your help!

- ✂

Unit Opening Letter
Magnets

Your name _____ Child's name _____

Home phone _____ Work phone _____

Use with Lesson 1,
Teaching Guide page A23.

Name _____

Magnetic Attraction

In your child's science class, we're exploring the kinds of objects that are attracted by magnets. You can explore magnetic attraction with your child, using objects in your home.

What You Need

✔ Magnet
✔ Small objects (metal spoon, glass jar, plastic container, nail, keys, metal paper clip, eraser, pencil)

What You Do

On the back of this sheet, make a chart like the one below and list the objects in the left-hand column. Have your child place a magnet near each object and carefully observe what happens. Help your child write yes or no in the right-hand column to indicate whether the object was attracted by the magnet.

What Happened?

Talk with your child about the kinds of objects that were attracted by the magnet. Help your child understand that objects made of iron or steel are attracted by magnets.

Please have your child return the completed chart to class.

Object	Attracted

© Silver Burdett Ginn

Use with Lesson 1, Teaching Guide page C23.

Name _____

Magnetic Force

In your child's science class, we're learning that magnetic force can pass through air and certain materials, making it possible to move objects without touching them.

What You Need

✔ Magnet
✔ Small object that contains steel or iron, such as a paper clip
✔ Flat, solid materials (paper, cardboard, plastic tray, ceramic dish)

What You Do

On the back of this sheet, make a chart like the one below and list the flat, solid materials in the left column. Invite your child to hold a magnet slightly above an object that contains iron or steel. Move the magnet and observe what happens. Then hold a sheet of paper between the magnet and the object; have your child hold the magnet slightly above the paper and move the magnet. Continue placing other materials between the metallic object and the magnet and having your child observe what happens when the magnet is moved.

What Happened?

Talk with your child about what happened. Help your child understand that the iron or steel object moved when magnetic force passed through some of the materials placed between the magnet and the object.

Please have your child return the completed chart to class.

Material	What Happens?

Use with Lesson 2,
Teaching Guide page C31.

Name _____

Magnetic Strength

In your child's science class, we're studying the magnetic strength of different magnets. You can explore the strength of magnets with your child, using objects around your home.

What You Need

✔ Magnets of various sizes and shapes
✔ Box of steel paper clips

What You Do

On the back of this sheet, make a chart like the one below and draw the different magnets in the left-hand column. Invite your child to dip one end of a magnet into the box of paper clips and then slowly pull it out. Help your child carefully pull off the clips

and count how many the magnet attracted. Then help your child record that number in the right-hand column on the chart. Try other magnets and record your results.

What Happened?

Talk with your child about the strength of each magnet. Help your child understand that the strongest magnet picked up the most paper clips.

Please have your child return the chart to class.

Magnet	Number of Paper Clips Attracted

© Silver Burdett Ginn

Use with Lesson 3,
Teaching Guide page C39.

Name _____

Magnetic Poles

In your child's science class, we're learning that every magnet has a north-seeking pole and a south-seeking pole. Opposite poles pull toward (or attract) each other, and like poles push away from (or repel) each other.

What You Need

✔ Magnets of various sizes and shapes

What You Do

Help your child test the poles of the magnets by bringing the end of one magnet close to the end of another magnet. Do the magnets pull together or push apart? Test different ends and sides of the same magnets to see if they act differently. On the back of this sheet, have your child draw two pictures: one that shows like poles attracting each other and one that shows unlike poles repelling each other. Help your child label the pictures, using the words *Like Poles* and *Unlike Poles*.

What Happened?

Talk with your child about the activity. Help your child understand

that when parts of two magnets are attracted to each other, one part is a south pole and one part is a north pole. When parts of magnets repel each other, the parts were either both north poles or both south poles.

Please have your child return the drawings to class.

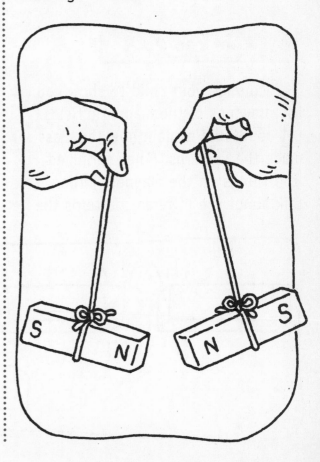

Use with Lesson 4,
Teaching Guide page C47.

Name _____

Magnetic Fields

In your child's science class, we're learning about the invisible forces that surround a magnet. Your child has drawn the patterns that iron filings make when they are placed near magnets. These patterns show the magnetic fields around the magnets.

What You Need

✔ Your child's drawings of patterns of iron filings around one magnet and around two magnets placed close together

What You Do

Encourage your child to show you the drawings of the magnetic fields. Let your child explain how the class made the patterns. (They sprinkled iron filings on the magnets.) Then talk about the different patterns the iron filings made when placed near one magnet and when placed near two magnets. Have your child mark *N* or *S* on the unmarked pole in each picture below.

What Happened?

Help your child understand that the drawings with two magnets show lines of magnetic force pushing apart when two like poles are near each other and pulling together when two unlike poles are together.

Please have your child return the drawings and this sheet to class.

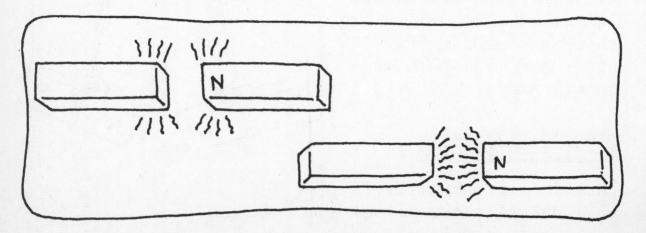

Use with Lesson 5, Teaching Guide page C55.

Name _____

Temporary Magnets

In your child's science class, we've made and used temporary magnets. You can make temporary magnets at home, using an old spoon and a magnet.

What You Need

✔ String
✔ Magnet
✔ Thin stick
✔ Paper clips
✔ Construction paper
✔ Old metal spoon
✔ Scissors
✔ Bowl or shoebox

What You Do

Wrap a long piece of string around the bowl of a spoon and tie it to a thin stick. Invite your child to cut out fish shapes from construction paper and attach a paper clip to the mouth of each fish. Put the fish in the bowl or shoebox. Help your child turn the spoon into a temporary magnet by stroking the handle at least 10 times in one direction with a household magnet. The more you stroke the spoon, the stronger the magnetic force will be. Let your child go fishing with a spoon! On the back of this sheet, help your child write one or two sentences about this activity.

What Happened?

Help your child understand that he or she made the spoon a temporary magnet by rubbing it with the household magnet. The temporary magnet behaves like a "real" magnet for a short time.

Please have your child return the sentences to class.

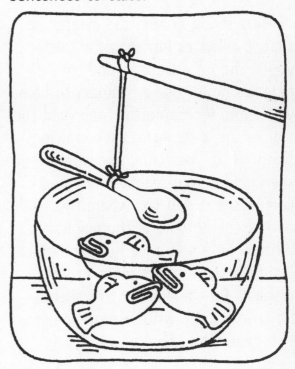

 Use with Lesson 6,
Teaching Guide page C63.

Name _____

A Magnet Compass

In your child's science class, we're learning that a compass is a kind of magnet that works because the north-seeking pole of a freely swinging magnet always points north.

What You Need

- ✔ Compass
- ✔ Bar magnet
- ✔ Small self-stick notes
- ✔ String
- ✔ Pencil

What You Do

Tie a string around the magnet so that it balances horizontally. Take your child on a walk around the neighborhood. Use a compass to help your child locate north. Then hold the magnet on a string so that it swings freely. Have your child use what he or she knows about magnets and compasses to tell you where the north-seeking pole of the magnet is. Write *N* on a self-stick note and place it on the appropriate place on the magnet. On the back of this sheet, have your child write a sentence or two about the activity.

What Happened?

Ask your child to tell you how a compass and a magnet are alike. Help your child understand that a compass is a kind of magnet, and when the magnet swings freely the north-seeking pole always points north.

Please have your child return the sentences to class.

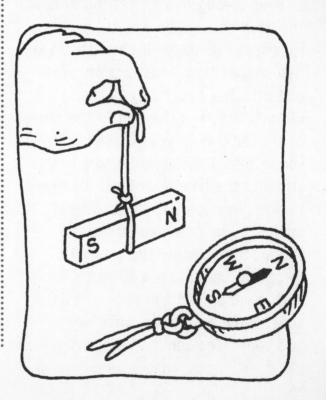

Dear Family,

We hope that you and your child have enjoyed finding out about magnets. Would you like to learn more about magnetic forces and how they help us every day? Here are some things you and your child can do together.

- Visit a TV or electronics store and talk to the manager about how magnets are used in electronic equipment.

- In an encyclopedia or other reference, find out how magnets and electricity combine to make electromagnets. How are these very strong magnets used to construct homes and office buildings?

- Using magnets, design and create your own games.

- Read more about it! These books can help you learn more about magnets.

The Science Book of Magnets
by Neil Ardley
(Harcourt Brace Jovanovich, 1991)

Magnets
by Jason Cooper
(The Source Corporation, 1992)

Exploring Magnets
by Ed Catherall
(Steck-Vaughn, 1990)

The Book of Magnets
by Mae Freeman
(Four Winds Press, 1985)

Experiments with Magnets
by Helen J. Challand
(Childrens Press, 1986)

Science Experiments
by Vera Webster
(Childrens Press, 1990)

OVERVIEW

Science Notebook

Recording information as it is observed is a key aspect of any scientific investigation. Recordings become primary data from which to draw conclusions, summarize research, double-check results, and plan future investigations. For children, knowing they will be recording data usually leads them to make more careful observations during an activity. They learn to look for important details that can support a concept or conclusion.

The **Science DiscoveryWorks** Science Notebook gives children an early opportunity to associate activities with recording data. By filling in charts, making graphs, drawing representations of results, and summarizing activities, children practice the data-collection techniques used at all levels of scientific inquiry. As added benefits, the recording of data provides children with a kinesthetic modality for learning, helps them organize their thinking, and provides a record for them to return to when they are preparing their portfolios.

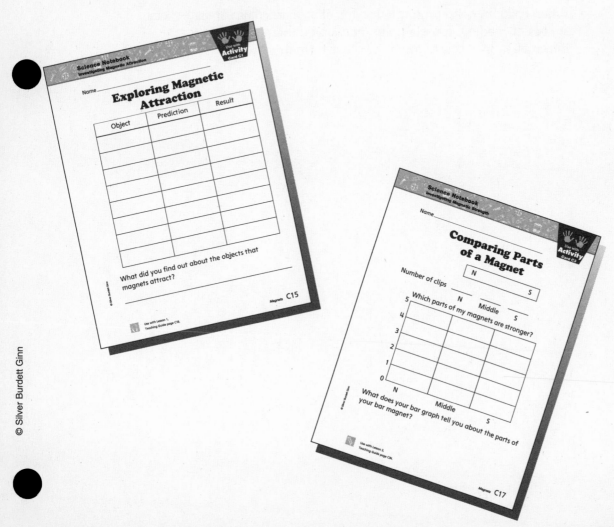

In the early school years, most children have little reason or opportunity to make lists or record data in their everyday experience. Making a list of party guests, taking brief telephone messages, or keeping score in a game may be their only chances to record data. You can help children build an appreciation for recording information by encouraging recording data through writing or drawing where it falls naturally in the school day.

- Help children make up and use score sheets for both quiet games and organized outdoor games.

- Let children participate in making and updating classroom charts and assignment sheets. Even a kindergartner can write his or her name on tag board and place it on a task chart on a bulletin board.

- Let children conduct interviews or surveys around the school and record the results on charts.

- When children collect information for other curriculum areas—social studies or reading, for example—encourage them to record the information in a chart, graph, or other format.

Name_____

Exploring Magnetic Attraction

Object	Prediction	Result

What did you find out about the objects that magnets attract?

_____

_____

Name _____

Discovering Magnetic Force

Object	What happened to the paper clip

Which objects made the clip fall? How are they alike?

_____

_____

Use with
Activity
Card C3

Name _____

Comparing Parts
of a Magnet

N	S

Number of clips

Which parts of my magnets are stronger?

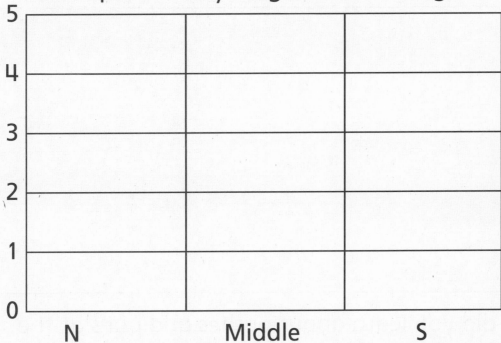

What does your bar graph tell you about the parts of your bar magnet?

_____

_____

Name_____

Observing the Poles of Magnets

1. _____

_____

2. _____

_____

3.

What did you learn about pushes and pulls at the
ends of the magnets?

_____

_____

Name _____

Making Magnetic Patterns

Drawing 1

Drawing 2

Drawing 3

How are your three drawings alike? How are they different?

_____

_____

_____

Use with Lesson 5,
Teaching Guide page C50.

Magnets C19

Name_____

Making Magnets

Drawing 1

Drawing 2

Compare your drawings. What happened to the spoon?

_____

_____

_____

Name_____

Using a Magnet as a Compass

What happened to the magnet?

Compare the magnet with the compass.

Magnet	Compass

How are the magnet and the compass alike?

_____

_____

Science Notebook

Answers

Name_____

Exploring Magnetic Attraction

Object	Prediction	Result
Possible answers:		
crayon	no	no
paper clip	yes	yes
pencil	no	yes

What did you find out about the objects that magnets attract?

The objects that magnets attract are all made of metal.

_____

Use with Lesson 1,
Teaching Guide page C18.

Magnets **C15**

Name_____

Discovering Magnetic Force

Object	What happened to the paper clip
	The paper clip will remain standing until a metallic object containing magnetic properties is tested.

Which objects made the clip fall? How are they alike?

Objects that made the clip fall were made of metal.

_____

C16 Magnets

Use with Lesson 2,
Teaching Guide page C26.

Name_____

Comparing Parts of a Magnet

N		S

Number of clips — Numbers will depend on the strength of the magnet. The middle will be zero.

N	Middle	S

Which parts of my magnets are stronger?

5

4   Columns *N* and *S* will show similar amounts filled in. The middle column should read zero.

3

2

1

0

| N | Middle | S |

What does your bar graph tell you about the parts of your bar magnet?

The ends of the magnet are stronger than the middle is. The middle does not hold any paper clips.

Use with Lesson 3,
Teaching Guide page C34.

Magnets **C17**

Name_____

Observing the Poles of Magnets

1. The magnets will either pull together or push apart.

_____

2. This answer should be the opposite of the result

obtained in 1.

3.

Drawings should show the magnets touching end to end with the poles labeled alternately *N* and *S*.

What did you learn about pushes and pulls at the ends of the magnets?

If the poles are the same, they will push away from each other; if they are different, they will pull together.

C18 Magnets

Use with Lesson 4,
Teaching Guide page C42.

Science Notebook

Answers

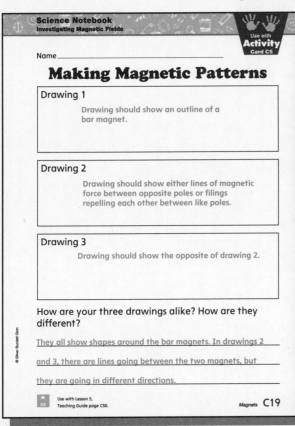

Science Notebook
Investigating Magnetic Fields

Use with **Activity** Card C5

Name_____

Making Magnetic Patterns

Drawing 1

Drawing should show an outline of a bar magnet.

Drawing 2

Drawing should show either lines of magnetic force between opposite poles or filings repelling each other between like poles.

Drawing 3

Drawing should show the opposite of drawing 2.

How are your three drawings alike? How are they different?

They all show shapes around the bar magnets. In drawings 2
and 3, there are lines going between the two magnets, but
they are going in different directions.

Use with Lesson 5,
Teaching Guide page C50.

Magnets C19

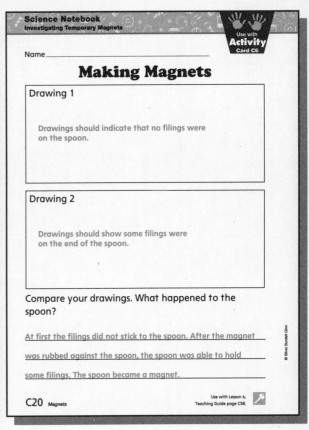

Science Notebook
Investigating Temporary Magnets

Use with **Activity** Card C6

Name_____

Making Magnets

Drawing 1

Drawings should indicate that no filings were on the spoon.

Drawing 2

Drawings should show some filings were on the end of the spoon.

Compare your drawings. What happened to the spoon?

At first the filings did not stick to the spoon. After the magnet

was rubbed against the spoon, the spoon was able to hold

some filings. The spoon became a magnet.

C20 *Magnets*

Use with Lesson 6,
Teaching Guide page C58.

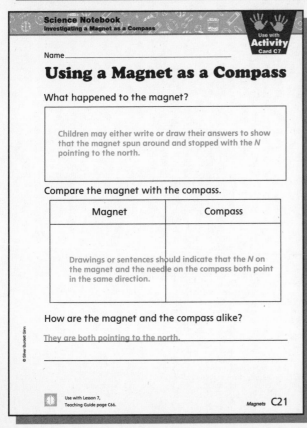

Science Notebook
Investigating a Magnet as a Compass

Use with **Activity** Card C7

Name_____

Using a Magnet as a Compass

What happened to the magnet?

Children may either write or draw their answers to show that the magnet spun around and stopped with the *N* pointing to the north.

Compare the magnet with the compass.

Magnet	Compass
Drawings or sentences should indicate that the *N* on the magnet and the needle on the compass both point in the same direction.	

How are the magnet and the compass alike?

They are both pointing to the north._____

_____

Use with Lesson 7,
Teaching Guide page C66.

Magnets C21

© Silver Burdett Ginn

Magnets C23

Activity Support

Recognizing that your school day is a busy one and that you want to spend your time with the children you teach rather than with paperwork, **Science DiscoveryWorks** provides a number of Activity Support pages to help you save time.

General-Use Pages

Scientists use many formats for recording the data they collect. To help children become accustomed to thinking about appropriate ways to record data, **Science DiscoveryWorks** provides five general-use Activity Support pages. Work that children do using these pages may become the basis for a portfolio selection.

2–cm Grid This grid can be adapted to a number of uses, including the following.

- When children need to compare numbers of objects, have them color in a square for each one of the first kind of object. Then have them use a second color to color in a square for each one of the second kind of object.

- Let children use the grid as a game board with a design and rules that they make up.

Word Web A word web with one main cell and four secondary cells can be adapted by adding more cells when needed. Here are some ways to use the word web.

- Use the web to help children understand vocabulary and main ideas. For example, if they write *Plants* in the main cell, they might write *Leaves, Stems, Roots,* and *Green* in the other cells.

- In small groups, have children use the web to keep track of assignments. For example, the activity can be written in the main cell, and the individuals and their tasks can be written in the secondary cells.

- Have children use the web as a pre-activity brainstorming tool. They can write a topic in the main cell and ideas they associate with the topic in the secondary cells.

Prediction/Result Since predicting and testing are important science skills, you may want to have children use this page often. Having a formal way of recording predictions and results gives children something concrete to look at when they think back on an activity.

Chart/Survey In the early grades, charts are used frequently to help children organize information. When children first begin to use the chart, you may want to block off columns or rows they do not need. Here are some hints for using the Chart/Survey page.

- Invite children to use the chart when they need to tally information about more than one item.

- When appropriate, show children how to use the chart to keep track of survey results. If necessary, have children tape two or more pages together.

- Where home-school letters call for families to develop separate recording charts, you may want to send home a copy of this page.

Venn Diagram Even though Venn diagrams have many sophisticated applications, children can use them to organize their thinking when they are comparing things. Here are some ideas for using Venn diagrams.

- Label parts of the diagram. For example, when children are comparing plants and animals, label the top circle *Plants*, the bottom circle *Animals*, and the center overlap *Both*. Then help children compare by writing characteristics in the correct places.

- Use the diagram to help children understand colors. For example, if children color one full circle red and the other yellow, they will see for themselves that orange is made by combining red and yellow.

Name _____

2-cm Grid

Name_____

Word Web

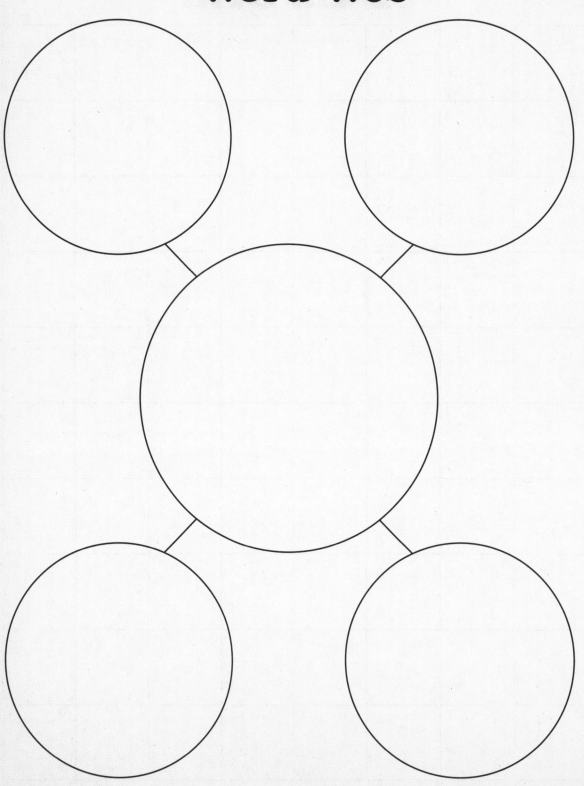

Use with Unit C,
Teaching Guide pages C1–C71.

Name_____

Prediction/Result

Prediction

Result

Name_____

Chart/Survey

Name_____

Venn Diagram

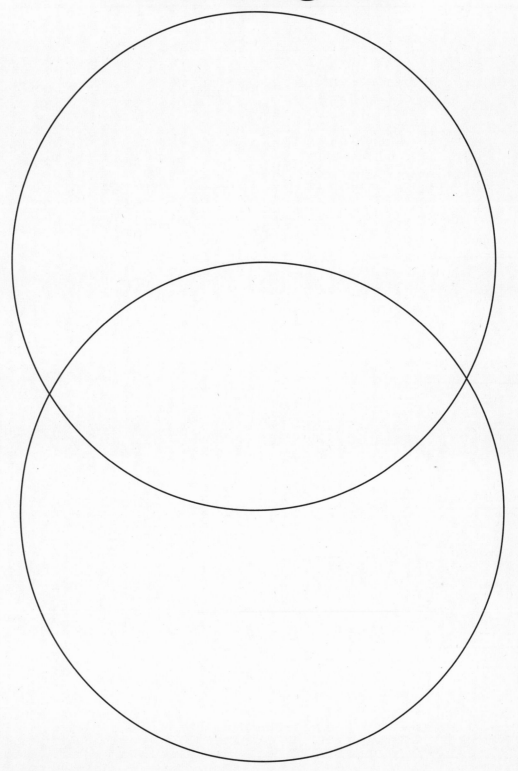

OVERVIEW
Assessment Guide

 The key to evaluating the success of any science program lies in assessment methods that help you and the children you teach measure progress toward instructional goals.

A varied assessment program can

- Help you determine which children need more help and where classroom instruction needs to be expanded.

- Help you judge how well children understand, apply, and communicate what they have learned.

- Provide children with strategies for monitoring their own progress and ways to demonstrate their talents and abilities.

Science DiscoveryWorks provides a comprehensive assessment package as shown below.

The *Science DiscoveryWorks* Assessment Package		
Objectives	**Assessments Available in *Science DiscoveryWorks***	**Sources in *Science DiscoveryWorks***
Develop process skills	Performance Assessment	TG, AG
	Observation and Interview	TG, AG
	Portfolio Assessment	TG, AG
	Self-Assessment	AG
Understand concepts	Observation and Interview	TG, AG
	Portfolio Assessment	TG, AG
	Lesson Assessment and Unit Test	AG
Develop scientific reasoning skills	Observation and Interview	TG, AG
Show individual or group progress	Portfolio Assessment	TG, AG
	Self-Assessment	AG
	Group Self-Assessment	TG, AG
Demonstrate effectiveness of instruction	Performance Assessment	TG, AG
	Portfolio Assessment	TG, AG
	Lesson Assessment and Unit Test	AG

Key: TG = Teaching Guide; AG = Assessment Guide

Overview of Assessments in This Guide

Science DiscoveryWorks provides many opportunities for you to evaluate how well the children in your class are learning science concepts and using science skills. Following are descriptions of the variety of assessment tools available.

Lesson Assessment

Purpose: Each Lesson Assessment measures children's understanding of the concept in that lesson.

Performance Assessment

Purpose: Performance Assessment helps you evaluate the skills and concepts developed through hands-on activities. *Science Discovery-Works* provides a formal Performance Assessment activity that should be used at the end of the unit.

- *Teacher Support page* gives you detailed instructions for administering the Performance Assessment.

- *Performance Assessment Support Page* provides drawings for children to use the Performance Assessment activity (provided only in units where necessary).

- *Recording Page* provides space on which children can record their observations and conclusions.

- *Scoring Checklist* helps you evaluate children's performance of the tasks in relation to stated goals.

Observation and Interview

Purpose: Observation and Interview allows you to document the day-to-day development of student understanding. Checklists allow you to organize and standardize the presentation of this information.

- *Science Process Skills Checklist* helps you record how well children apply science process skills during activities and formal performance tasks.

- *Group Skills Checklist* helps you summarize children's abilities to work in collaboration with others.

- *Scientific Reasoning Skills Checklist* provides a record of children's progress in demonstrating science and critical-thinking processes.

- *Concept Checklist* for each lesson helps you quickly record evidence of children's concept mastery.

Portfolio Assessment

Purpose: Portfolio Assessment provides a way of demonstrating a child's progress and development over time.

- *Inside My Science Portfolio* helps children explain why they want to include specific items in their portfolios.

- *Science Portfolio Evaluation Sheet* provides a chart for recording how children's portfolios demonstrate growth.

Self-Assessment

Purpose: Self-Assessment provides a method for analyzing and evaluating one's own strengths and weaknesses.

- *Self-Assessment Checklist* offers children a way to evaluate their own work and growth by rating themselves on a list of criteria.

- *Group Self-Assessment Checklist* helps children analyze their group skills as they rate themselves on specific criteria.

Unit Test

Purpose: Unit Test measures children's understanding and retention of concepts throughout an entire unit.

- A four-page written test is provided for each unit.

Lesson Assessment

In **Science DiscoveryWorks,** there are many opportunities for you to evaluate how well children in your class are learning science skills and concepts on a regular basis. Lesson Assessments give you early opportunities to identify children who need extra help so that you can plan for reteaching or for careful monitoring in subsequent lessons on related content.

Lesson Assessments measure children's understanding and retention of the lesson concepts. You may wish to use a Lesson Assessment in any of the following ways.

- As a pretest to establish a baseline assessment.

- As a posttest to determine children's progress toward understanding the lesson concept.

- As a review sheet to ensure greater retention of the lesson concept.

- As homework to reinforce the lesson concept.

Lesson Assessments are tailored to each level of reading readiness—from beginning to independent new readers. The Lesson Assessments reflect three carefully developed approaches that maximize the power to assess at each level.

- At the Kindergarten level, children are asked to ring pictures, to add to a picture, or to draw a picture in response to directions that you read aloud to them. A box at the bottom of each page gives you directions for administering each part of the assessment.

- The Grade 1 Lesson Assessments take a similar pictorial approach but include questions or statements directed to the child. A direction box at the bottom of each page gives you instructions for administering the assessment.

- The Grade 2 Lesson Assessments direct all questions and instructions to the child in language for the appropriate reading level. Questions call for children to write or draw their answers.

Following the Lesson Assessments you will find comprehensive answer sheets. For open-ended questions, where children could give a varied set of answers, the sheets give examples of possible responses.

Name_____

1. Which things could not be attracted by a magnet?

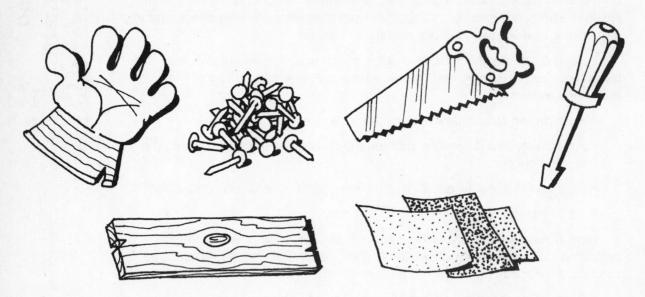

2. Which one thing could be attracted by the magnet?

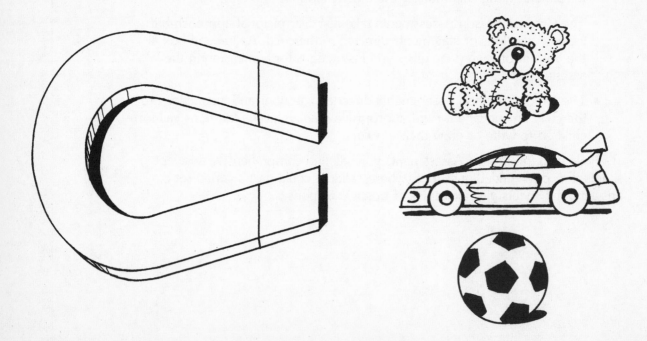

Directions: **1.** Have children ring each object that they think would *not* be attracted by a magnet.
2. Have children draw a line from the magnet to the object that could be attracted by a magnet.

Name_____

1. Which paper clip cannot be moved by the magnet below it?

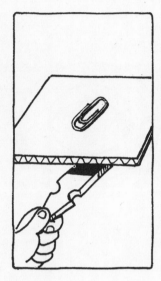 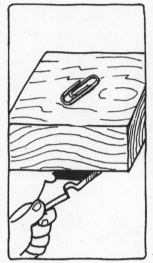 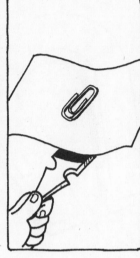 

2. Which boat could be moved by a magnet under the river?

Directions: **1.** Have children ring the paper clip that could not be moved by the magnet below it.
2. Have children ring the boat that could be moved by a magnet below the river, without touching the boat.

Name_____

1. Which parts of the magnets are the strongest?

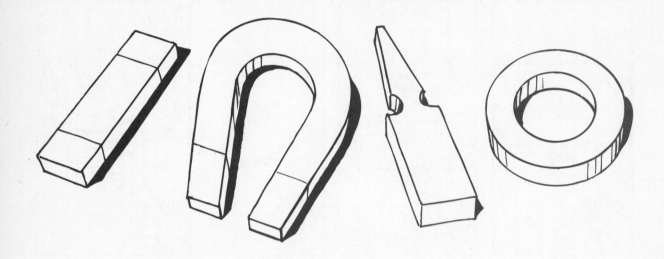

2. Which magnet is the strongest?

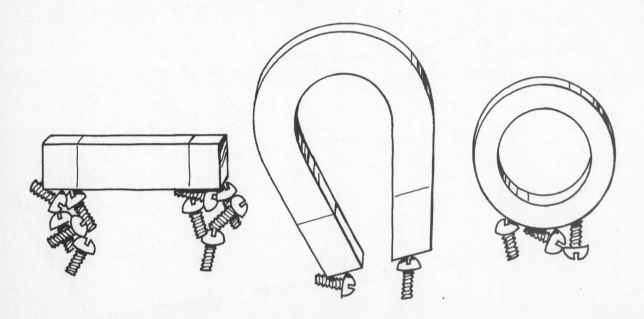

Directions: **1.** Have children color the strongest part of each magnet. **2.** Have children ring the strongest magnet.

Use with Lesson 3,
Teaching Guide pages C36–C37.

Name_____

1. Where are the north and south poles on the magnets?

2. Which train car would connect to the train next?

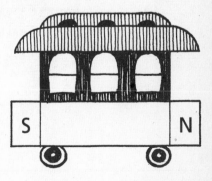

Directions: **1.** Have children finish labeling the poles on the row of magnets. **2.** Have children ring the train car that would be able to connect to the end of the train.

Name_____

1. Which magnet could make this pattern?

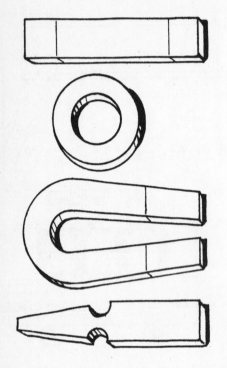
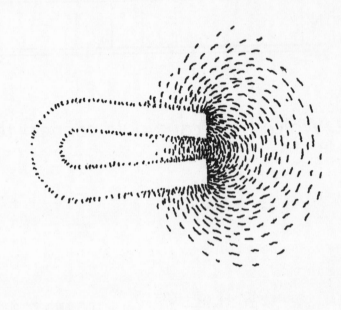

2. Which patterns were made with bar magnets?

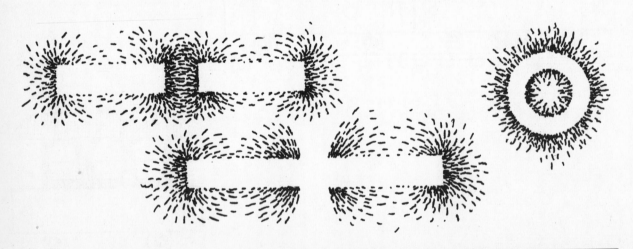

Directions: **1.** Have children ring the magnet that could have been used to make the iron-filing pattern that is pictured. **2.** Have children ring each pattern of iron filings that could have been made with bar magnets.

Use with Lesson 5,
Teaching Guide pages C52–C53.

Name_____

1. What should be the order of the pictures?

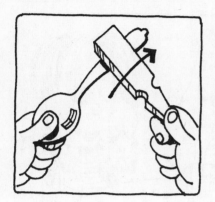 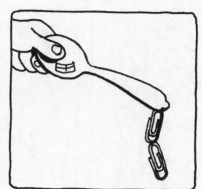 

_____ _____ _____

2. Which things could be made into a temporary magnet?

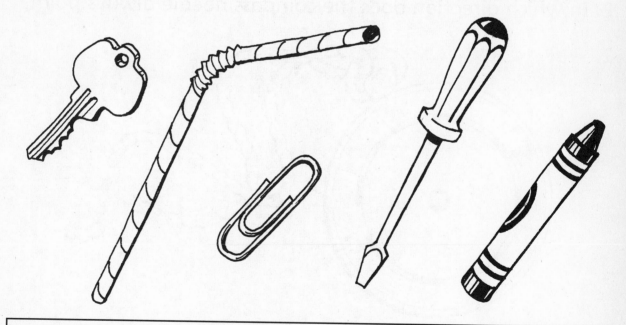

Directions: **1.** Have children write a number (1, 2, or 3) below each picture to indicate which is the first, second, and third step for making a temporary magnet. **2.** Have children ring each object that could be made into a temporary magnet.

Name_____

1. Which people will need to use a compass?

2. In which direction does the compass needle always point?

Directions: 1. Have children put an X on the picture where a compass could be helpful. **2.** Have children draw an arrow on the compass to show in which direction a compass needle points.

Answers

Lesson 1 Assessment
Magnets

Name_____

1. Which things could not be attracted by a magnet?

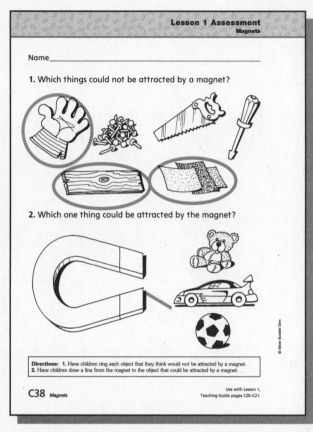

2. Which one thing could be attracted by the magnet?

Directions: 1. Have children ring each object that they think would *not* be attracted by a magnet.
2. Have children draw a line from the magnet to the object that could be attracted by a magnet.

C38 *Magnets*

Use with Lesson 1,
Teaching Guide pages C20–C21.

Lesson 2 Assessment
Magnets

Name_____

1. Which paper clip cannot be moved by the magnet below it?

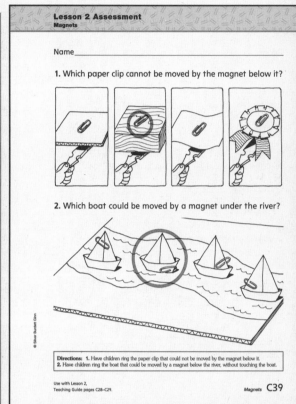

2. Which boat could be moved by a magnet under the river?

Directions: 1. Have children ring the paper clip that could not be moved by the magnet below it.
2. Have children ring the boat that could be moved by a magnet below the river, without touching the boat.

Use with Lesson 2,
Teaching Guide pages C28–C29.

Magnets C39

Lesson 3 Assessment
Magnets

Name_____

1. Which parts of the magnets are the strongest?

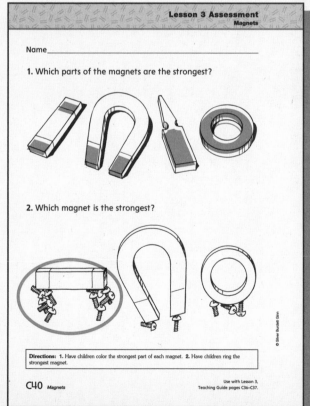

2. Which magnet is the strongest?

Directions: 1. Have children color the strongest part of each magnet. **2.** Have children ring the strongest magnet.

C40 *Magnets*

Use with Lesson 3,
Teaching Guide pages C36–C37.

Lesson 4 Assessment
Magnets

Name_____

1. Where are the north and south poles on the magnets?

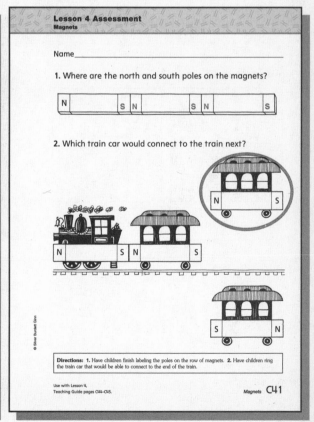

2. Which train car would connect to the train next?

Directions: 1. Have children finish labeling the poles on the row of magnets. **2.** Have children ring the train car that would be able to connect to the end of the train.

Use with Lesson 4,
Teaching Guide pages C44–C45.

Magnets C41

Answers

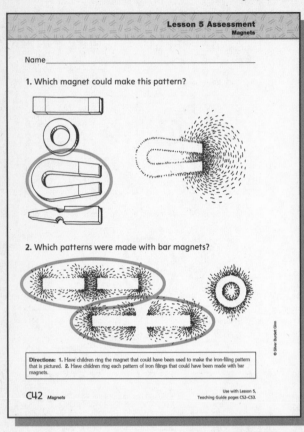

Lesson 5 Assessment
Magnets

Name_____

1. Which magnet could make this pattern?

2. Which patterns were made with bar magnets?

Directions: 1. Have children ring the magnet that could have been used to make the iron-filing pattern that is pictured. **2.** Have children ring each pattern of iron filings that could have been made with bar magnets.

C42 *Magnets*

Use with Lesson 5,
Teaching Guide pages C52–C53.

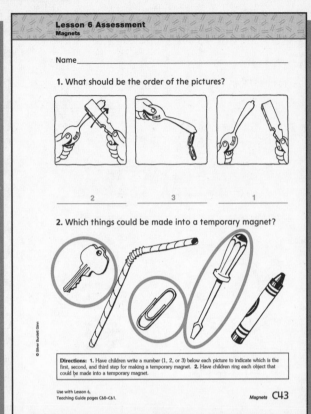

Lesson 6 Assessment
Magnets

Name_____

1. What should be the order of the pictures?

2   3   1

2. Which things could be made into a temporary magnet?

Directions: 1. Have children write a number (1, 2, or 3) below each picture to indicate which is the first, second, and third step for making a temporary magnet. **2.** Have children ring each object that could be made into a temporary magnet.

Use with Lesson 6,
Teaching Guide pages C60–C61.

Magnets C43

Lesson 7 Assessment
Magnets

Name_____

1. Which people will need to use a compass?

2. In which direction does the compass needle always point?

Directions: 1. Have children put an X on the picture where a compass could be helpful. **2.** Have children draw an arrow on the compass to show in which direction a compass needle points.

C44 *Magnets*

Use with Lesson 7,
Teaching Guide pages C68–C69.

Performance Assessment

Using Performance Assessment

Performance Assessment allows you to evaluate how well children apply their scientific knowledge and skills in different contexts and realistic situations. Performance Assessments in *Science DiscoveryWorks* offer children opportunities for

- Interactions in real-world settings.

- Discovery of alternative solutions to open-ended problems.

- Using a variety of materials and equipment.

- Focusing on ideas that reflect the main science themes.

- Interdisciplinary learning.

Using the Performance Assessment

The Performance Assessment is designed to be administered at the end of each unit. It includes a Teacher Support page with directions for administering the assessment, a Recording Page where children record their observations and conclusions, and a Checklist to help you assess children's performance-assessment task. Here are some tips for using the Performance Assessment.

- Before using the Performance Assessment, check the Teacher Support page for directions and any materials needed. Set up stations, if necessary.

- In terms that children understand, explain what the task is and how you will evaluate it. Encourage children to think through the task before beginning it.

- Keep in mind that Performance Assessment should be flexible. Children who perform equally well may work in different ways and require different amounts of time.

- Use the Checklist to evaluate children's performance, based upon observation, the Recording Page, or both.

Using Ongoing Performance Assessment

In the Teaching Guide, you will find regular opportunities to evaluate children's performance in the Assess Performance section of each lesson. The Process Skills Checklist and the Group Skills Checklist referred to under the Assess Performance heading appear in the Observation and Interview section of this guide.

Where's the Pole?
....

Children observe and experiment to find the poles of a wand magnet and other unmarked magnets. They also communicate their results.

Process Skills: Observe, Communicate, Experiment

Pacing: 20 minutes

Grouping: 1–4 children

Materials
- Bar magnets, with the poles clearly marked
- Wand magnet and other unmarked magnets
- Paper clip
- String
- Recording Page

Procedure

Ask children to find the poles on the marked bar magnet. Then let children explore with the magnets to identify the poles on the unmarked magnets. Ask children to tell what they found out. Have them draw or write on the Recording Page what they did and their results.

Circulate among the children to assess each child's efforts. Let children know that you will help with procedures if needed.

For Best Results: Encourage children to keep the materials away from the table edge.

Answers

1. Drawings should indicate that children used the marked bar magnet to test the wand magnet and the other unmarked magnets, finding out which poles repelled and which poles attracted.

2. Children's answers should indicate that they discovered the north and south poles of the wand magnet and the other unmarked magnets.

© Silver Burdett Ginn

Name_____

Where's the Pole?

1. Show what you did.

2. Tell what you learned.

_____

_____

_____

_____

Checklist
Performance Assessment

Children	Observe		Communicate		Experiment	
	Understands properties of materials used	Responds based on observations	Indicates a procedure on Recording Page	Indicates a result on Recording Page	Does more than one experiment	Relates results to observations

Scoring Rubric: **3**   Demonstrates mastery of skills/concepts required by activity
2   Demonstrates partial understanding of skills/concepts required by activity
1   Does not demonstrate understanding of skills/concepts required by activity

Use with Unit C,
Teaching Guide page C15.

Observation and Interview

Classroom observation and interview form the core of assessment because your experience as a teacher is your most important tool in evaluating the growth of your students. Most forms of assessment—performance assessment; portfolio assessment; individual, group, and self-assessment—derive their authenticity from the observations you and the children you teach make in the classroom. This section of the Assessment Guide includes checklists to help you make classroom observation and interview part of your overall assessment strategy.

Using Observation

The Science Process Skills Checklist, Group Skills Checklist, Scientific Reasoning Skills Checklist, and Concept Checklists can be used to document children's understanding of science skills and concepts and their growth and performance in working with classmates. Completed checklists will help you make lesson plans, assign projects, conduct conferences with children and parents, and form cooperative groups for future activities. Here are some tips for using classroom observation.

- Let children know that you will be observing them as they perform science activities. Classroom observation fosters the attitude in children that instruction and assessment go hand-in-hand.

- Reinforce the idea that science is learned as much by doing as it is by reading.

- Check the Teaching Guide for suggestions on where in the lesson to use the checklists.

- Try to observe children several times to identify any patterns and to allow children sufficient opportunity to show their strengths.

The **Science Process Skills Checklist** is designed to assess science process skills as children use them in activities as well as performance-assessment tasks. Here are some tips for using the Science Process Skills Checklist.

- Preview the Teaching Guide to determine which process skills are emphasized in each activity.

- Use a checklist for each activity. Then fill in the checklist with the names of the children in your class.

- You may want to carry the checklist with you and record as you observe.

The **Group Skills Checklist** gives you criteria for evaluating how children work together on science activities. Here are some tips for using the Group Skills Checklist.

- Use the checklist for activities where groupings are called for.

- Focus on only one or two small groups in each activity.

- Encourage children to tell you what they like best and least about working in a group. Then use this information to help children develop better group skills.

The **Scientific Reasoning Skills Checklist** is based on the work of the American Association for the Advancement of Science, which has identified certain values, attitudes, and skills associated with learning that can be used as benchmarks for acquiring science literacy. **Science DiscoveryWorks** is designed to foster the following scientific reasoning skills.

1. Longing to know and understand: the desire to probe, find information, and seek explanations

2. Questioning of scientific assumptions: the tendency to hold open for further verification of presented assumptions

3. Search for data and its meaning: the tendency to collect information and to analyze it in context

4. Demand for verification: the inclination to repeat and replicate findings and studies

5. Respect for logic: the inclination to move from assumptions to testing and from data collection to conclusions

6. Consideration of premises: the tendency to put into context the reason for a particular point of view

7. Consideration of consequences: the tendency to put into perspective the results of a particular point of view

8. Respect for historical contributions: the inclination to learn from the contributions of earlier ideas

Here are some tips for using the Scientific Reasoning Skills Checklist.

- Preview lessons in the Teaching Guide to find questions indicated by this symbol: ■. Decide if you will assess only those scientific reasoning skills noted by the symbol or if you will include others on the checklist.

- In addition to the questions in the Teaching Guide, ask questions that make children think about different facets of a situation: What really happened? What might happen now? How can you find out more?

- Some of the best moments will be "aha" experiences that occur unexpectedly (sometimes with children from whom you least expect it). For that reason, keep a copy of the checklist handy.

Using Interviews

You probably interview children informally as a regular part of your teaching day, so you know that interviewing is a useful technique for assessing both what children are learning and how effectively you are teaching a concept. To use the interview as a more formal assessment tool, set aside time when you can talk to a child individually, preferably when other children are not around.

Here are some specific suggestions for each lesson in this unit. As you interview the child, use the Concept Checklist for that lesson as a guide for asking questions. Then record your assessment of the child's understanding.

- **Lesson 1** Provide the child with a magnet and a selection of metallic and nonmetallic objects. Ask the child to predict which objects will be attracted by the magnet. Then have the child use the magnet to test the prediction and explain what happened.

- **Lesson 2** Give the child magnets of different strengths, thick and thin cardboard, and small objects that are attracted by magnets. Have the child predict which magnets will attract objects through the thick and the thin cardboard. Then have the child test the predictions and explain what happened.

- **Lesson 3** Show the child several magnets of different sizes, shapes, and strengths. Have the child predict which magnet is the strongest. Then provide paper clips, safety pins, or other metallic objects and have the child use the magnets to test the prediction.

- **Lesson 4** Label the north pole of a bar magnet. Then provide the child with the labeled bar magnet and two or three other magnets. Have the child use the bar magnet to test the other magnets to find the north pole of each magnet.

- **Lesson 5** Provide the child with several magnets, some iron filings in a shaker, and a sheet of paper. Have the child place one magnet at a time on the paper and sprinkle it with iron filings. Have the child explain what each pattern of filings shows.

- **Lesson 6** Give the child a magnet, a metallic object (such as a nail or a screwdriver), and some small metallic objects (such as paper clips or safety pins). Have the child show you a way to make a temporary magnet to pick up the paper clips or safety pins.

- **Lesson 7** Provide the child with a compass and a bar magnet swinging freely from a string. Using the Lesson 7 Concept Checklist as a guide, ask the child questions about the direction that the compass and the magnet face.

Observation Checklist
Science Process Skills

Children	Observe	Classify	Measure and Use Numbers	Communicate	Infer	Predict	Collect, Record & Interpret Data	Identify and Control Variables	Define Operationally	Make Hypotheses	Experiment	Make and Use a Model

Scoring Rubric:
3 Demonstrates understanding of skill
2 Demonstrates partial understanding of skill
1 Does not demonstrate understanding of skill

Use with Unit C,
Teaching Guide pages C1–C71.

Observation Checklist
Group Skills

Children	Listens to Others	Participates in Discussion	Communicates Clearly	Shares Tasks	Takes Initiative	Shares Responsibility

Scoring Rubric:
3 Demonstrates excellent group skills
2 Demonstrates satisfactory group skills
1 Does not demonstrate satisfactory group skills

Observation Checklist
Scientific Reasoning Skills

Children	Longing to Know and Understand	Questioning of Scientific Assumptions	Search for Data and Its Meaning	Demand for Verification	Respect for Logic	Consideration of Premises	Consideration of Consequences	Respect for Historical Contributions

Scoring Rubric:
3 Demonstrates development of scientific reasoning skills
2 Demonstrates partial development of scientific reasoning skills
1 Does not demonstrate development of scientific reasoning skills

Use with Unit C,
Teaching Guide pages C1–C71.

Lesson 1: Concept Checklist
Magnets

Children	Concepts	
	Understands that objects can be classified as attracted by or not attracted by magnets	Recognizes that the ability to be attracted or not attracted by magnets is a property of an object

Scoring Rubric:
3 Demonstrates understanding of concept/skill
2 Demonstrates partial understanding of concept/skill
1 Does not demonstrate understanding of concept/skill

© Silver Burdett Ginn

Use with Lesson 1,
Teaching Guide page C21.

Lesson 2: Concept Checklist
Magnets

Children	Concepts			
	Realizes that magnets have magnetic force	Realizes that some magnets have more force than others	Understands that a magnet can move an object without touching it	Realizes that magnetic force can pass through some materials and not others

Scoring Rubric:
3 Demonstrates understanding of concept/skill
2 Demonstrates partial understanding of concept/skill
1 Does not demonstrate understanding of concept/skill

© Silver Burdett Ginn

Lesson 3: Concept Checklist
Magnets

	Concepts	
Children	**Understands that magnets have different strengths**	**Understands that you can't tell the strength of a magnet by looking at its size or shape**

Scoring Rubric:
3 Demonstrates understanding of concept/skill
2 Demonstrates partial understanding of concept/skill
1 Does not demonstrate understanding of concept/skill

© Silver Burdett Ginn

Lesson 4: Concept Checklist
Magnets

Children	Concepts			
	Understands that a magnet has two poles	Understands unlike poles attract; like poles repel	Understands toys push apart if like poles face	Understands toys pull together if unlike poles face

Scoring Rubric: **3** Demonstrates understanding of concept/skill
2 Demonstrates partial understanding of concept/skill
1 Does not demonstrate understanding of concept/skill

Use with Lesson 4,
Teaching Guide page C45.

Lesson 5: Concept Checklist
Magnets

Children	Concepts	
	Understands that the pattern of iron filings show the magnetic fields and how the force of the magnet works	Understands that iron filings show a picture or model of the lines of magnetic force, not the actual magnetic field

Scoring Rubric:
3 Demonstrates understanding of concept/skill
2 Demonstrates partial understanding of concept/skill
1 Does not demonstrate understanding of concept/skill

Lesson 6: Concept Checklist
Magnets

Children	Concepts		
	Recognizes that only objects attracted by a magnet can become temporary magnets	Recognizes that a permanent magnet must be used to make a temporary magnet	Realizes that temporary magnets won't remain magnets forever

Scoring Rubric:
3 Demonstrates understanding of concept/skill
2 Demonstrates partial understanding of concept/skill
1 Does not demonstrate understanding of concept/skill

Use with Lesson 6, Teaching Guide page C61.

Lesson 7: Concept Checklist
Magnets

Children	Concepts		
	Understands that a freely moving bar magnet and a compass always point north	Infers that a compass is a tiny bar magnet	Understands why a compass is useful

Scoring Rubric:
3 Demonstrates understanding of concept/skill
2 Demonstrates partial understanding of concept/skill
1 Does not demonstrate understanding of concept/skill

Portfolio Assessment

Portfolios give children the opportunity to showcase their best efforts in a collection of their work. Unlike a test, which gives a picture of children's achievements at a certain point in time, portfolios provide evidence of progress over a period of time. In addition, portfolios can also serve the following purposes.

- Give insight into children's views of themselves through the specific pieces they choose to include.

- Enable you to communicate more effectively with family members about children's work.

- Encourage children to join with you in assessing their work.

- Collectively provide tools for evaluating instruction and curriculum.

Throughout the school year, children can be compiling a working portfolio. At specified times, such as the end of a grading period or the end of a unit, children should review what they have in their portfolios to select what they want to include in a final portfolio.

The items that go into a portfolio should be carefully chosen. A portfolio generally contains examples of required work, such as completed tests, which demonstrate children's abilities to solve problems and use science process skills. Also, it usually includes creative work, such as Science Notebook pages, original models, and stories or essays. Here are some additional examples.

- Information from Investigate Further activities

- Data from integrated-curriculum projects

- Drawings or graphs

- Pictures or photographs

- Audiotapes or videotapes

- Unit Project results

- Performance Assessment Recording Pages

This guide provides evaluation sheets for both you and your students to assess their portfolios. Inside My Science Portfolio helps children show their favorite selections. The Science Portfolio Evaluation Sheet helps you determine how a portfolio's contents demonstrate growth in different science areas.

Give each child a copy of the Inside My Science Portfolio page. Provide a time for children to evaluate the material in their portfolios. Suggest that children consider ideas such as these when they make their selections.

- I thought this would be too hard, but I did it!

- This needed real teamwork.

- I would like to share this with a friend.

- I would like to do this again in a different way.

- This was fun!

Fill out the Science Portfolio Evaluation Sheet for each child. Keep in mind the following four growth areas as you look through each portfolio.

- What evidence is there that the child is using science process skills?

- What science concepts are covered in the portfolio?

- How has the child progressed in his or her ability to work in groups?

- In what ways has the child shown development of scientific reasoning skills?

Here are some tips for using the Portfolio Assessment.

- Plan a class session on how to build portfolios. Ask children to help brainstorm some of the kinds of items they may want to keep.

- Develop a list of do's and don'ts, such as: Do always date the items. Don't include every piece of work.

- Have available a variety of art materials for completing Inside My Science Portfolio.

- Respond to children's portfolios. Let children know if you plan to use the portfolios during conferences with their families.

Name _____

Inside My
Science Portfolio
· ·

I worked by myself.

I worked with a group.

Name_____

Science Portfolio
Evaluation Sheet
···

Growth Area	How Portfolio Demonstrates Growth
Science Process Skills	
Science Concepts	
Group Skills	
Scientific Reasoning Skills	

Additional Comments

_____

_____

_____

_____

Use with Unit C,
Teaching Guide pages C1–C71.

Self-Assessment

When children are asked to evaluate and monitor their own work, they are using self-assessment. Effective self-assessment can build children's confidence as well as give them a sense of control over their own learning.

Science DiscoveryWorks provides two self-assessment checklists.

The *Self-Assessment Checklist* is a good opportunity for children to reflect on their performance or understanding. It can be used after an activity or at the end of a unit. As children become accustomed to filling out the checklist, they will seek to demonstrate the positive approaches listed there.

The *Group Self-Assessment Checklist* provides children with the opportunity to evaluate the work of a group. Individuals observe the dynamics of group interaction and reflect on how their own contributions to group work made a difference.

Here are some tips for using the checklists.

- After completing the first activity, hand out the Self-Assessment Checklist. Review the statements and the rating system. Explain that the checklists are meant to help each child find out more about herself or himself.

- Ask children to think about what they did and what they learned from the activity. Encourage them to rate themselves honestly, emphasizing that there are no "right" answers to the individual items.

- You may discover that some children are more critical of themselves than they need to be. Consider tailoring the Self-Assessment Checklist for children to use in observing others. Children may get more positive feedback of their performance than they would give themselves. Emphasize that children should evaluate work, not the personalities of others.

- Encourage groups to use the Group Self-Assessment Checklist occasionally for specified cooperative-learning activities. You might wish to model use of the checklist during an activity to give children an idea of what to look for. In future activities, suggest that group members take turns being the evaluator.

Name_____

Child's Checklist
·······························

Circle the face that shows how well you worked.

1. I followed directions.

2. I helped my group.

3. I was careful.

4. I was a good listener.

5. I asked questions.

What I Liked Most	What I Want to Learn

Use with Unit C,
Teaching Guide pages C1–C71.

Name_____

Group Checklist

Circle the face that shows how well your group worked.

1. We listened to each other.

2. We worked carefully.

3. We all worked.

4. We helped each other.

5. We all cleaned up.

What Our Group Did Best	What We Need to Work On

Unit Test

....

Throughout the **Science DiscoveryWorks** teaching cycle, you will find built-in opportunities for assessing skill and concept attainment on a regular and ongoing basis. The written Unit Test provided in this Assessment Guide gives you an instrument for assessing, scoring, and recording a child's concept mastery over an entire and discrete unit of instruction.

To evaluate children's comprehension of specific science concepts, the four-page test uses a carefully designed mixture of objective questions and art to cover each lesson concept from the unit. You not only get the whole picture of children's understanding but also assign a score to their responses.

You will find that **Science DiscoveryWorks** gives you evaluation tools that are tailored to each level of reading readiness—from beginning to independent new readers. The tests reflect three carefully developed approaches that maximize their power to assess at that level.

At the Kindergarten level, children will be asked to ring pictures in response to questions, to add to a picture, or to draw a picture in response to a question that you read aloud to them. A box at the bottom of the page gives you directions for administering each part of the test.

The Grade 1 Unit Tests take a similar pictorial approach but include questions directed to the child. A direction box at the bottom of the page gives you instructions for administering the test.

The Grade 2 Unit Tests direct all questions and instructions to the child in language at the appropriate reading level. Questions call for children to write or draw their answers.

Following each Unit Test, you will find a comprehensive answer sheet for that test. For open-ended questions, where children could give a varied set of answers, the sheet gives examples of possible responses.

Name_____

1. Which things will be attracted by magnets?

2. Which one could you put
   between the ball and the
   magnet to make the ball fall?

Directions: 1. Have children put an X on the pictured objects they think will be attracted by a magnet. **2.** Have children ring the object that would break the magnetic force and let the ball fall down.

Name _____

3. Which magnet is the strongest?

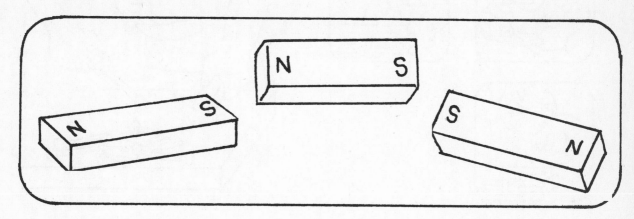

4. What part of each magnet will be attracted by the north pole of this magnet?

Directions: **3.** Have children put an X on the magnet that has the most magnetic force.
4. Have children put an X on the pole of each pictured magnet where it will be attracted by the top magnet's north pole.

Name_____

5. Where will the magnet most attract a paper clip?

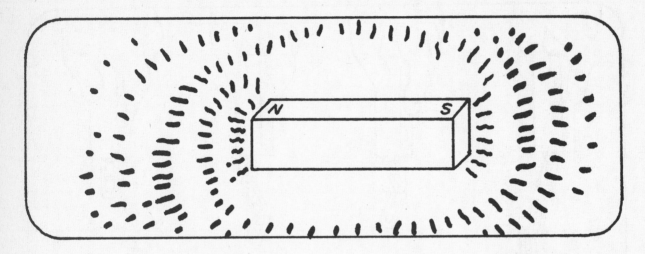

6. How could you make the nails stick to the screwdriver?

Directions: **5.** Have children put X's where paper clips would be most attracted by the magnet.
6. Describe each action pictured—rubbing the screwdriver with a nail; hitting the screwdriver with the magnet; stroking the screwdriver with the magnet several times in the same direction. Have children ring the action that would make the screwdriver magnetic.

Name_____

7. What things are north of the whale?

| **Directions:** | **7.** Describe the art. Have children find and label North on the map. Have them put an X on the things that are north of the whale. |

Unit Test

······················· Answers ·······················

Unit Test
Magnets

Name_____

1. Which things will be attracted by magnets?

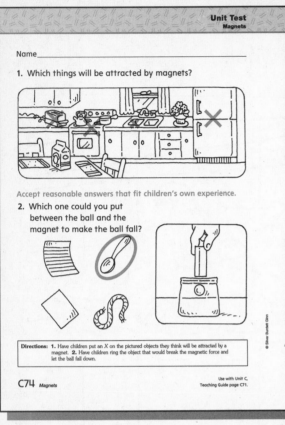

Accept reasonable answers that fit children's own experience.

2. Which one could you put
   between the ball and the
   magnet to make the ball fall?

Directions: 1. Have children put an X on the pictured objects they think will be attracted by a magnet. 2. Have children ring the object that would break the magnetic force and let the ball fall down.

C74 *Magnets*

Use with Unit C,
Teaching Guide page C71.

© Silver Burdett Ginn

Unit Test
Magnets

Name_____

3. Which magnet is the strongest?

4. What part of each magnet will be attracted by the north pole of this magnet?

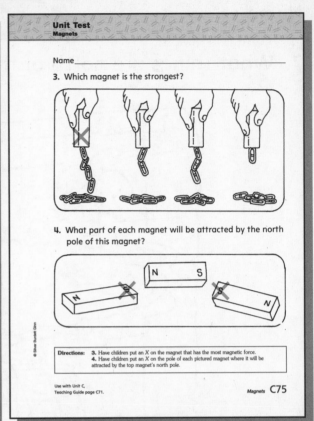

Directions: 3. Have children put an X on the magnet that has the most magnetic force.
4. Have children put an X on the pole of each pictured magnet where it will be attracted by the top magnet's north pole.

Use with Unit C,
Teaching Guide page C71.

Magnets C75

© Silver Burdett Ginn

Unit Test
Magnets

Name_____

5. Where will the magnet most attract a paper clip?

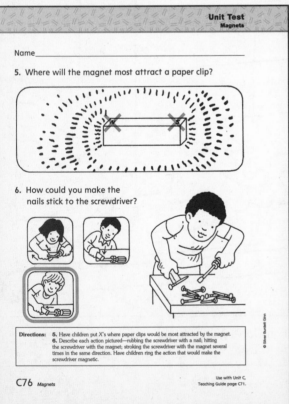

6. How could you make the
   nails stick to the screwdriver?

Directions: 5. Have children put X's where paper clips would be most attracted by the magnet.
6. Describe each action pictured—rubbing the screwdriver with a nail; hitting the screwdriver with the magnet; stroking the screwdriver with the magnet several times in the same direction. Have children ring the action that would make the screwdriver magnetic.

C76 *Magnets*

Use with Unit C,
Teaching Guide page C71.

© Silver Burdett Ginn

Unit Test
Magnets

Name_____

7. What things are north of the whale?

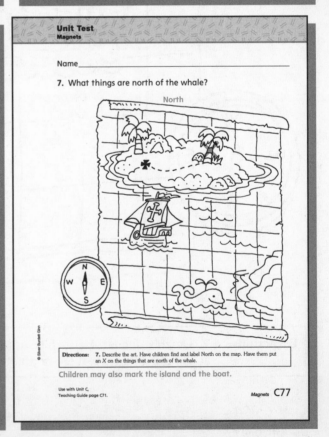

Directions: 7. Describe the art. Have children find and label North on the map. Have them put an X on the things that are north of the whale.

Children may also mark the island and the boat.

Use with Unit C,
Teaching Guide page C71.

Magnets C77

© Silver Burdett Ginn

Unit Project Pages

Science *DiscoveryWorks* helps you fulfill your curricular goals by offering you and your class both long-term and short-term science activities. While individual lesson activities give children plenty of hands-on experiences, the Unit Project adds a new dimension by building from lesson to lesson. The Unit Project gives children a chance to apply new concepts to an ongoing project—and gives you a unique opportunity for observation. The cumulative nature of the project lets you emphasize how each new lesson fits into the larger picture, not only of the project, but of the world outside the classroom.

In a Unit Project, children might create a "museum for the senses," give a weather report, or construct a database of living things. Whatever the format, Unit Projects emphasize putting unit concepts into context. Through these projects, children not only learn to apply their knowledge, but also learn how to build on what they have already absorbed. The projects offer an excellent opportunity to study children's growth and their ability to work on a sustained undertaking.

Unit Project Introduction

Every Unit Project begins with an overview of the project and a brief summary of each Unit Project Link. It suggests the optimum grouping and lets you know what materials you will need. The Unit Project introduction for the *Magnets* unit appears on page C13 of the Teaching Guide.

Unit Project Links

Each project includes a number of steps that build to a culminating activity. So you can easily see how the activities in the Unit Project relate to material covered in the unit, each activity is linked directly to a particular lesson. Each project step requires children to apply concepts from a lesson to the project. The Unit Project Links for the *Magnets* unit appear on pages C22, C30, C46, C62, and C70 of the Teaching Guide.

Unit Project Pages

Unit Project Pages included in this Teacher Resource Book are blackline masters that can be photocopied for the entire class. They are matched to Unit Project Links and might serve any of the following functions: as worksheets integral to the Unit Project Links activities; as rough drafts of artwork; or as alternatives to original artwork.

Unit Project Scoring Checklist

Following the Unit Project Pages in this Teacher Resource Book, you will find a Unit Project Scoring Checklist with guidelines for evaluating children's performance and assigning a numerical value. While each **Science Discovery-Works** Unit Project offers children a long-term project to stimulate and challenge them, it also gives you a chance to assess children's performance on a task that spans multiple lesson cycles.

Magnet Puppets

City Scenery

Use with Lesson 2,
Teaching Guide page C30.

How Magnets Act

Making Temporary Magnets

Object	Results

Use with Lesson 6,
Teaching Guide page C62.

Using a Compass

_____

_____

Scoring Checklist
Unit Project

Children	Completes Task	Understands Concepts	Applies Science Processes	Communicates With Group

Scoring Rubric:
3 Performance exceeds all criteria of the project.
2 Performance meets the criteria of the project.
1 Performance is inappropriate or incomplete.

Use with Unit C,
Teaching Guide pages C1–C71.

Teacher Notes

_____

_____

_____

_____

_____

_____

_____

_____

_____

_____

_____

_____

_____

_____

_____

_____

Teacher Notes

Teacher Notes

Teacher Notes

Teacher Notes

Teacher Notes